Dedicated
to those
learning to count

MY BERMUDA

1, 2, 3

by Dana Cooper

One moon

shines in the sky

Two palms

bend to the west

Three bluebirds

nest up high

As Four lizards

lie down to rest

Five shells

wash up in a wave

Shark Oil

Shark balm

6

Six sharks

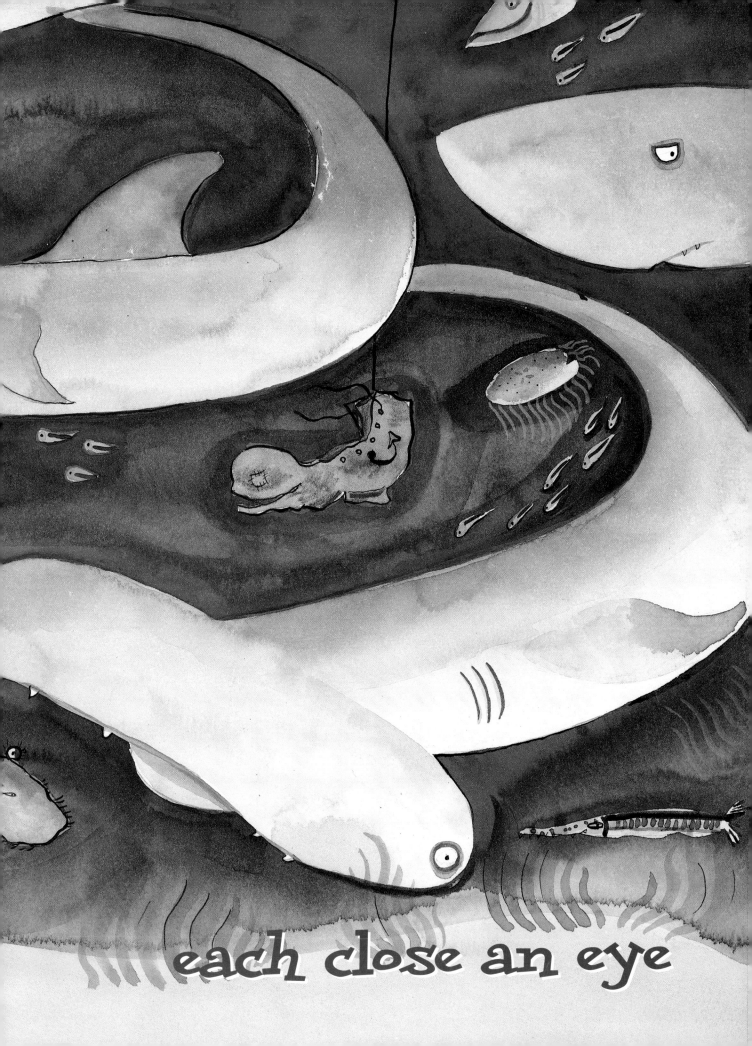

each close an eye

Seven crabbies

huddle in a cave

While Eight jellyfish

slowly slip by

Nine angels

whisper in the wind

Ten glow-worms

light up the sea

11

Eleven mermaids

drift double-finned

As Twelve stars

shine down on me

The End